LANGUAGE!

Practice

Student Workbook B
Units 7-12

Judy Fell Woods, SLP, MA

04   03   02   01   11   10   9   8

ISBN # 1-57035-142-2

Text layout and cover design by Susan Fogo
Edited by Raven Moore
Illustrations by Peggy Ranson

Printed in the United States of America

Published and distributed by

SOPRIS
WEST

4093 Specialty Place • Longmont, CO 80504 • (303) 651-2829
www.sopriswest.com

107BKB/5-01/KEN/7.5M

Table of Contents

Unit Concepts

<u>qu</u>, <u>x</u>, <u>y</u>, <u>z</u>

Practice reading and spelling these words every day. Use the practice methods your teacher shows you. Then use each word aloud in a sentence. You can do it!

and	quit	yip
fix	sax	zap
Max	six	zig-zag
mix	tax	zip
quack	wax	
quick	yap	

Phoneme-Grapheme Correspondence Activity:
Phoneme Isolation 1

Listen to each word your teacher says. Underline the first letter of each word.

1.   r   p   s

2.   t   p   f

3.   x   b   s

4.   a   y   qu

5.   c   d   g

6.   h   j   qu

7.   f   k   l

8.   m   i   n

9.   p   s   r

10.   v   b   w

Phoneme-Grapheme Correspondence Activity:
Phoneme Isolation 2

Write the first letter of each word your teacher says. Look at the alphabet list here if you need help.

abcdefghijklmnopqrstuvwxyz

1. _____

2. _____

3. _____

4. _____

5. _____

6. _____

7. _____

8. _____

9. _____

10. _____

11. _____

12. _____

13. _____

14. _____

15. _____

Writing Practice: q

Listen to your teacher's directions as you trace and copy this letter.
Put your pencil on the dot to begin.

q   •   •   •   •

q   •   •   •   •

q   •   •   •   •

q   •   •   •   •

Writing Practice: <u>u</u>

Listen to your teacher's directions as you trace and copy this letter.
Put your pencil on the dot to begin.

u

u

u

u

Writing Practice: x

Listen to your teacher's directions as you trace and copy this letter. Put your pencil on the dot to begin.

X

X

X

X

Writing Practice: y

Listen to your teacher's directions as you trace and copy this letter.
Put your pencil on the dot to begin.

y

y

y

y

Writing Practice: z

Listen to your teacher's directions as you trace and copy this letter.
Put your pencil on the dot to begin.

Z · · · ·

Z · · · ·

Z · · · ·

Z · · · ·

Spelling Words Practice

1. Write and say each word three times.
2. Say the meaning or meanings for each word, and use each word aloud in a sentence.

quack, quick, quit, six, sax, wax, tax, fix

1.

2.

3.

4.

5.

6.

7.

8.

mix, Max, yaps, zig-zag, zip, yip, zaps, and

9. _____

10. _____

11. _____

12. _____

13. _____

14. _____

15. _____

16. _____

Phoneme Segmentation

1. Read each word aloud.
2. Divide each word into beginning, middle, and ending sounds.
   (Remember: **qu** stands for two beginning sounds, */kw/*.
   ck stands for the ending sound, */k/*.)
3. Write the entire word.

Read the Word	Divide the Sounds			Write the Word
	Beginning	Middle	End	
1. quack				
2. quick				
3. quit				
4. six				
5. sax				
6. wax				
7. tax				

Read the Word	Divide the Sounds			Write the Word
	Beginning	Middle	End	
8. fix				
9. mix				
10. zap				
11. Max				
12. yap				
13. yip				
14. zig				

Spelling Words in Sentences

Use each word in a written sentence. Don't forget to use capital letters and correct ending punctuation.

quack, quit, six, tax, Max, zig-zag, yip

1.

2.

3.

4.

5.

6.

7.

Word Search

Find each hidden word. Some words might be hiding more than once, so make sure you mark them all!

1. quit	sritnjdoquitalwodmrqut
2. tax	stldkfeotueoataxfjetaxa
3. zip	caftzipiorotuzopzipwuei
4. wax	yasoeithjdiyawaxkdowax

Matching

Draw a line from each word to the picture that matches it.

six

quack

wax

Max

zig-zag

Picture-a-Word

1. Draw a picture for each of these words.
2. Use each word aloud in a sentence.

sax	yap
six	zig-zag

Mixed-Up Words

Fix these mixed-up words and then write each one in a sentence.
Use the word list here to help you.

yap, quack, wax, six, Max

1. xwa

2. ckaqu

3. pya

4. xMa

yap, quack, wax, six, Max

5. isx   _____

Mixed-Up Sentences

Fix these mixed-up sentences and write them correctly.
(*Hint:* The words with the capital letters, question marks, and periods will help you.)

1. zig-zags. van The

   _____

   -

   _____

2. can yap. Max

   _____

   -

   _____

3. Max cat. the is

   _____

   -

   _____

Words in Alphabetical Order

Arrange these words in alphabetical order.

quit, fix, yip, Max, and, sax

a b c d e f g h i j k l m n o p q r s t u v w x y z

1. _____

2. _____

3. _____

4. _____

5. _____

6. _____

Cloze Sentences

Find and circle the word that finishes each sentence.

1. The six kids _____ and yap in the back.
   A) quick
   B) yip

2. The van zig-_____ and hits a cab!
   A) zags
   B) yaps

3. Pat, Tam, Al, Kim, Sam, and _____ ran into the van.
   A) Nick
   B) Pick

4. The fat cat is _____.
   A) quit
   B) quick

5. The tin can had bad ham and _____.
   A) yams
   B) yips

6. The van had a _____ fix.
   A) quack
   B) quick

7. Sam can fix a bit of the _____.
   A) fix
   B) mix

Editor in Chief

Write a <u>C</u> on the line after the word if it is correct. If the word is spelled wrong, write it correctly on the line.

1. quak

2. quick

3. wix

4. tix

5. yap

6. zig-zagg

7. Maxx

8. six

Story Writing

1. Write a story using some of the words from this unit.
2. If you wish, use another sheet of paper to draw pictures for your story or to make it longer.
3. Write a title for your story.

Unit Concept

<u>o</u>

Practice reading and spelling these words every day. Use the practice methods your teacher shows you. Then use each word aloud in a sentence. You can do it!

Bob	hop	not
box	hot	on
dock	rob	rock
dog	job	sock
fox	jog	Tom

Word Monster: *was*

Writing Practice: o

Listen to your teacher's directions as you trace and copy this
letter. Put your pencil on the dot to begin.

O

O

O

O

Spelling Words Practice

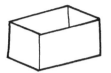

1. Write and say each word three times.
2. Say the meaning or meanings for each word, and use each word aloud in a sentence.

job, Tom, box, not, hot, dog, Bob, rob

1.

2.

3.

4.

5.

6.

7.

8.

Spelling Words Practice (continued)

fox, on, jog, sock, rock, hop, dock, was

9.

10.

11.

12.

13.

14.

15.

16.

Phoneme Segmentation

1. Read each word aloud.
2. Divide each word into beginning, middle, and ending sounds.
3. Write the entire word.

Read the Word	Divide the Sounds			Write the Word
	Beginning	Middle	End	
1. job				
2. rob				
3. Tom				
4. box				
5. not				
6. hot				
7. dog				

Phoneme Segmentation (continued)

Read the Word	Divide the Sounds			Write the Word
	Beginning	Middle	End	
8. Bob	_____	_____	_____	_____
9. fox	_____	_____	_____	_____
10. on	_____	_____	_____	_____
11. jog	_____	_____	_____	_____
12. cob	_____	_____	_____	_____
13. sock	_____	_____	_____	_____
14. rock	_____	_____	_____	_____
15. dock	_____	_____	_____	_____

Spelling Words in Sentences

Use each word in a written sentence. Don't forget to use capital letters and correct ending punctuation.

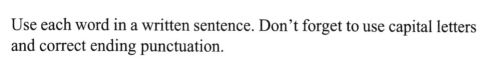

job, box, hot dog, Bob, dock, jog, on

1. _____

2. _____

3. _____

4. _____

5. _____

6. _____

7. _____

Word Search

Find each hidden word. Some words might be hiding more than once, so make sure you mark them all!

1. job	aoitrijobhritojejihjobjesl
2. not	palsioeotunotsehtirodsp
3. rob	crobritopwrobjrutirrodcjr
4. rock	qapofugirockutirickturock

Matching

Draw a line from each word to the picture that matches it.

jog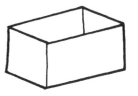

dog

sock

box

hot dog

Picture-a-Word

1. Draw a picture for each of these words.
2. Use each word aloud in a sentence.

jog	hop
dog	sock

Mixed-Up Words

Fix these mixed-up words and then write each one in a sentence. Use the word list here to help you.

Mom, sock, hot, nod, lock

1. sokc

2. mMo

3. don

4. colk

Mom, sock, hot, nod, lock

5. tho

_____

_____

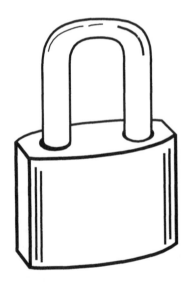

Mixed-Up Sentences

Fix these mixed-up sentences and write them correctly. (*Hint:* The words with the capital letters, question marks, and periods will help you.)

1. Pop nap. has a

   _____

   -

   _____

2. picks Tom on Max.

   _____

   -

   _____

3. cot. Tab is the on

   _____

   -

   _____

Words in Alphabetical Order

Arrange these words in alphabetical order.

job, Bob, on, Tom, rock, dog

a b c d e f g h i j k l m n o p q r s t u v w x y z

1. _____

2. _____

3. _____

4. _____

5. _____

6. _____

Cloze Sentences

Find and circle the word that finishes each sentence.

1. Al said to Dad, " I am _____ sick."   A) lot
   B) not

2. The fat cat sat on the _____ top!   A) box
   B) lox

3. "Quick. Fix the _____ dog," Sis said.   A) top
   B) hot

4. _____ and Max have a bit of a nap.   A) Pop
   B) Did

5. Sam hops on top of the _____.   A) nod
   B) dock

6. Sam, Tam, and Max _____ in the back of the taxi.   A) hot
   B) got

7. "Tab is _____ a bad dog," said Tam and Sam.    A) hot
   B) not

Editor in Chief

Write a <u>C</u> on the line after the word if it is correct. If the word is spelled wrong, write it correctly on the line.

1. jobb

2. Tom

3. hhot

4. boxx

5. kob

6. hop

7. fox

8. rok

Story Writing

1. Write a story using some of the words from this unit.
2. If you wish, use another sheet of paper to draw pictures for your story or to make it longer.
3. Write a title for your story.

Unit Concepts

-ss, **-ll**, **-ff**, **-zz**

Practice reading and spelling these words every day. Use the practice method your teacher shows you. Then use each word aloud in a sentence. You can do it!

Bill	Jill	pill
doll	kiss	quill
fizz	miss	stiff
hill	muff	will
hiss	off	
jazz	pass	

Word Monster: *you*

Phoneme-Grapheme Correspondence Activity:
Phoneme Isolation

Listen to each word your teacher says. Underline the last sound you hear in each word.

1.　　ss　　　　ll　　　　zz

2.　　zz　　　　ss　　　　ll

3.　　ff　　　　ll　　　　ss

4.　　ss　　　　zz　　　　ff

5.　　ff　　　　ss　　　　ll

6.　　ff　　　　zz　　　　ss

7.　　ll　　　　ss　　　　ff

8.　　ss　　　　ll　　　　zz

9.　　ss　　　　ff　　　　ll

10.　　zz　　　　ss　　　　ff

Spelling Words Practice

1. Write and say each word three times.
2. Say the meaning or meanings for each word and use each word aloud in a sentence.

miss, kiss, hiss, Quill Pass, pill, Bill, will, hill

1.

2.

3.

4.

5.

6.

7.

8.

Jill, jazz, fizz, doll, off, stiff, muff, you

9.

10.

11.

12.

13.

14.

15.

16.

Phoneme Segmentation

1. Read each word aloud.
2. Divide each word into beginning, middle, and ending sounds.
3. Write the entire word.

Read the Word	Divide the Sounds			Write the Word
	Beginning	Middle	End	
1. miss				
2. kiss				
3. hiss				
4. quill				
5. pass				
6. pill				
7. will				

Phoneme Segmentation (continued)

Read the Word	Divide the Sounds			Write the Word
	Beginning	Middle	End	
8. Bill				
9. hill				
10. jazz				
11. fizz				
12. off				
13. muff				
14. doll				
15. Jill				

Spelling Words in Sentences

Use each word in a written sentence. Don't forget to use capital letters and correct ending punctuation.

miss, hill, muff, will, jazz, you, doll

1.

2.

3.

4.

5.

6.

7.

Word Search

Find each hidden word. Some words might be hiding more than once, so make sure you mark them all!

1.	miss	missnjfuridomissodkem
2.	will	fheiswillwoeirhsilleidowk
3.	stiff	hisoestijirstidorstiffstifflei
4.	jazz	pisiwaskjisjazzjfiojagojazz

Matching

Draw a line from each word to the picture that matches it.

Bill

Jill

doll

kiss

hill

Picture-a-Word

1. Draw a picture for each of these words.
2. Use each word aloud in a sentence.

muff

kiss

pill

fizz

Mixed-Up Words

Fix these mixed-up words and then write each one in a sentence.
Use the word list here to help you.

Miss, Jill, off, jazz, will, fizz, Bill, doll

1. siMs

_____

2. lliw

_____

3. zajz

_____

4. fof

_____

Mixed-Up Words (continued)

Miss, Jill, off, jazz, will, fizz, Bill, doll

5. lJil

Mixed-Up Sentences

Fix these mixed-up sentences and write them correctly. (*Hint:* The words with the capital letters, question marks, and periods will help you.)

1. Pin tack on map. the a

2. box sill. is on the The

3. Jill. Pass doll to the

4. kiss? Can have I a

5. Bill tap will Jill.

Words in Alphabetical Order

Arrange these words in alphabetical order.

miss, kiss, hiss, jazz, fizz, will, you, off, pill, Bill

a b c d e f g h i j k l m n o p q r s t u v w x y z

1. _____

2. _____

3. _____

4. _____

5. _____

6. _____

7. _____

8. _____

9. _____

10. _____

Cloze Sentences

Find and circle the word that finishes each sentence.

1. Kim can tack a pin on the
   map at Quill _____.

   A) Pass
   B) Let

2. "The pin is not on the map,"
   said _____ Pitt.

   A) Mass
   B) Miss

3. Sis can _____ the doll to Jill and Bill.

   A) pass
   B) less

4. Bill can toss his jack-in-the-box
   at _____.

   A) Jill
   B) quick

5. "Can I have the _____, Tam?" said Sis.

   A) doll
   B) hill

6. I _____ sit at the back till I win.

   A) pill
   B) will

7. "I can _____ you on
   the hill," said Al.

   A) lass
   B) pass

Editor in Chief

Write a <u>C</u> on the line after the word if it is correct. If the word is spelled wrong, write it correctly on the line.

1. miss

2. kis

3. wil

4. Bil

5. jazz

6. fiz

7. yu

8. stif

Story Writing

1. Write a story using some of the words from this unit.
2. If you wish, use another sheet of paper to draw pictures for your story or to make it longer.
3. Write a title for your story.

Unit Concepts

-ng, **-nk**

Practice reading and spelling these words every day. Use the practice method your teacher shows you. Then use each word aloud in a sentence. You can do it!

bang	rang	sink
bank	rank	song
gang	ring	tank
honk	rink	wing
king	sank	yank
long	sing	

Word Monster: *what*

Phoneme-Grapheme Correspondence Activity:
Phoneme Isolation

Listen to each word your teacher says. Write the first letter of each word.

1. _____

2. _____

3. _____

4. _____

5. _____

6. _____

7. _____

8. _____

9. _____

10. _____

11. _____

12. _____

13. _____

14. _____

15. _____

16. _____

17. _____

18. _____

19. _____

20. _____

Spelling Words Practice

1. Write and say each word three times.
2. Say the meaning or meanings for each word, and use each word aloud in a sentence.

sing, song, ring, long, rang, king, bang, gang

1.

2.

3.

4.

5.

6.

7.

8.

wing, bank, yank, tank, rink, sink, honk, rank

9. _____ _____ _____

10. _____ _____ _____

11. _____ _____ _____

12. _____ _____ _____

13. _____ _____ _____

14. _____ _____ _____

15. _____ _____ _____

16. _____ _____ _____

sank, what

17. _____ _____ _____

18. _____ _____ _____

Phoneme Segmentation

1. Read each word aloud.
2. Divide each word into beginning, middle, and ending sounds. The dotted line will help you divide the ending sounds.
3. Write the entire word.

Read the Word	Divide the Sounds			Write the Word
	Beginning	Middle	End	
1. sing	s	i	ng	sing
2. song				
3. ring				
4. long				
5. rang				
6. king				
7. bang				

Read the Word	**Divide the Sounds**			**Write the Word**
	Beginning	Middle	End	

8. gang

9. yank

10. tank

11. rink

12. sink

13. honk

14. rank

15. sank

Spelling Words in Sentences

Use each word in a written sentence. Don't forget to use capital letters and correct ending punctuation.

sing, ring, long, king, bank, sink, what

1. _____

2. _____

3. _____

4. _____

5. _____

6. _____

7. _____

Word Search

Find each hidden word. Some words might be hiding more than once, so make sure you mark them all!

1.	song	songsingsinghiodkesong
2.	rang	stlkjfrangaksdrrangdkeot
3.	honk	honkdroeidyhondruehonkr
4.	rank	eisurielslraneiosrankkresn

Matching

Draw a line from each word to the picture that matches it.

ring

king

wing

tank

gang

Picture-a-Word

1. Draw a picture for each of these words.
2. Use each word aloud in a sentence.

sing	bang
bank	rink

Mixed-Up Words

Fix these mixed-up words and then write each one in a sentence. Use the word list here to help you.

ring, king, honk, pink, gang, wink, bank, link

1. nrig

2. nkho

3. knig

4. npik

Mixed-Up Words (continued)

ring, king, honk, pink, gang, wink, bank, link

5. ggna   _____

Mixed-Up Sentences

Fix these mixed-up sentences and write them correctly. (*Hint:* The word with the capital letters, question marks, and periods will help you.)

1. not bang! Do

2. a song. will Kim sing

3. at is the Sid rink

4. king! the am I

5. Sam box. locks the

Words in Alphabetical Order

Arrange these words in alphabetical order.

what, long, ring, bank, yank, honk, king, gang, tank, song

a b c d e f g h i j k l m n o p q r s t u v w x y z

1. _____

2. _____

3. _____

4. _____

5. _____

6. _____

7. _____

8. _____

9. _____

10. _____

Cloze Sentences

Find and circle the word that finishes each sentence.

1. Pam has _____, hot pink socks.

   A) long
   B) pong

2. "Fill the gas _____ in the cab," said the hack man.

   A) think
   B) tank

3. The bad pan sat in the _____.

   A) sank
   B) sink

4. The gang was at the _____.

   A) rink
   B) ring

5. Sam can pass the pack of kids as if his back had _____.

   A) sings
   B) wings

6. The _____ of the Rink is the kid to pass the pack.

   A) Wing
   B) King

7. Kim will sing a long, sad _____.

   A) gong
   B) song

Editor in Chief

Write a <u>C</u> on the line after the word if it is correct. If the word is spelled wrong, write it correctly on the line.

1. sing

2. ranng

3. king

4. tenk

5. honmk

6. whut

7. sink

8. rinnk

Story Writing

1. Write a story using some of the words from this unit.
2. If you wish, use another sheet of paper to draw pictures for your story or to make it longer.
3. Write a title for your story.

Unit Concepts

wh, **th**, **sh**, **ch**

Practice reading and spelling these words every day. Use the practice methods your teacher shows you. Then use each word aloud in a sentence. You can do it!

cash	shall	this
chat	ship	wham
chill	shock	whiff
fish	Thad	with
math	than	
rich	think	

Word Monsters: *are, put*

Spelling Words Practice

1. Write and say each word three times.
2. Say the meaning or meanings for each word, and use each word aloud in a sentence.

this, Thad, think, than, whiff, wham, chill, math

1.

2.

3.

4.

5.

6.

7.

8.

Spelling Words Practice (continued)

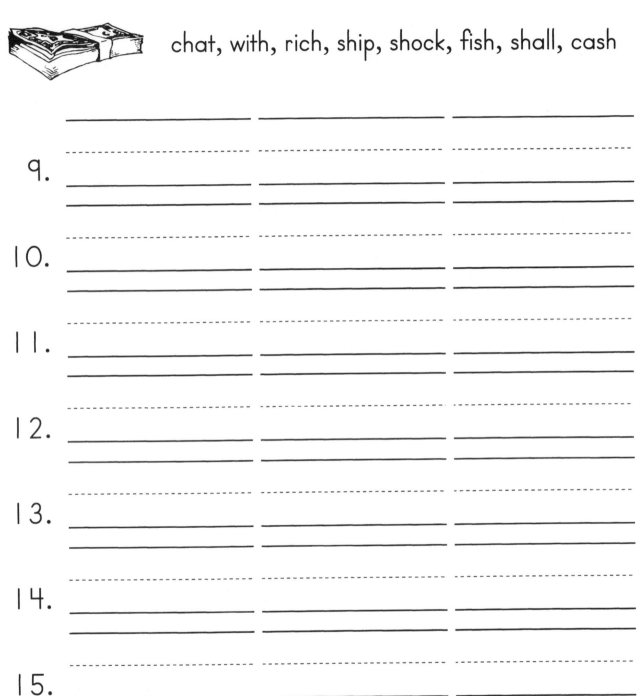

chat, with, rich, ship, shock, fish, shall, cash

9. _____ _____ _____

10. _____ _____ _____

11. _____ _____ _____

12. _____ _____ _____

13. _____ _____ _____

14. _____ _____ _____

15. _____ _____ _____

16. _____ _____ _____

are, put

17. _____

18. _____

Phoneme Segmentation

1. Read each word aloud.
2. Divide each word into beginning, middle, and ending sounds.
3. Write the entire word.

Read the Word	Divide the Sounds			Write the Word
	Beginning	Middle	End	
1. this				
2. chill				
3. ship				
4. Thad				
5. math				
6. shock				
7. thick				

Phoneme Segmentation (continued)

Read the Word	Divide the Sounds			Write the Word
	Beginning	Middle	End	
	___	___	___	___
8. chat	___	___	___	___
9. fish	___	___	___	___
10. than	___	___	___	___
11. with	___	___	___	___
12. shall	___	___	___	___
13. whiff	___	___	___	___
14. wham	___	___	___	___
15. cash	___	___	___	___

Spelling Words in Sentences

Use each word in a written sentence. Don't forget to use capital letters and correct ending punctuation.

this, ship, think, chat, fish, are, put

1. _____

2. _____

3. _____

4. _____

5. _____

6. _____

7. _____

Word Search

Find each hidden word. Some words might be hiding more than once, so make sure you mark them all!

1.	this	thisthasthisthosthosthis
2.	chill	chirleiodchidleichillchills
3.	stock	shakestockshrtedstockei
4.	think	tresuthiuthinkrheisoewks

Matching

Draw a line from each word to the picture that matches it.

ship

Thad

math

fish

cash

Picture-a-Word

1. Draw a picture for each of these words.
2. Use each word aloud in a sentence.

chat	whiff
rich	wham

Mixed-Up Words

Fix these mixed-up words and then write each one in a sentence. Use the word list here to help you.

wham, fish, math, thing, chap

1. hcpa

2. nigth

3. mtha

4. sfih

wham, fish, math, thing, chap

5. mawh

Mixed-Up Sentences

Fix these mixed-up sentences and write them correctly. (*Hint:* The words with the capital letters, question marks, and periods will help you.)

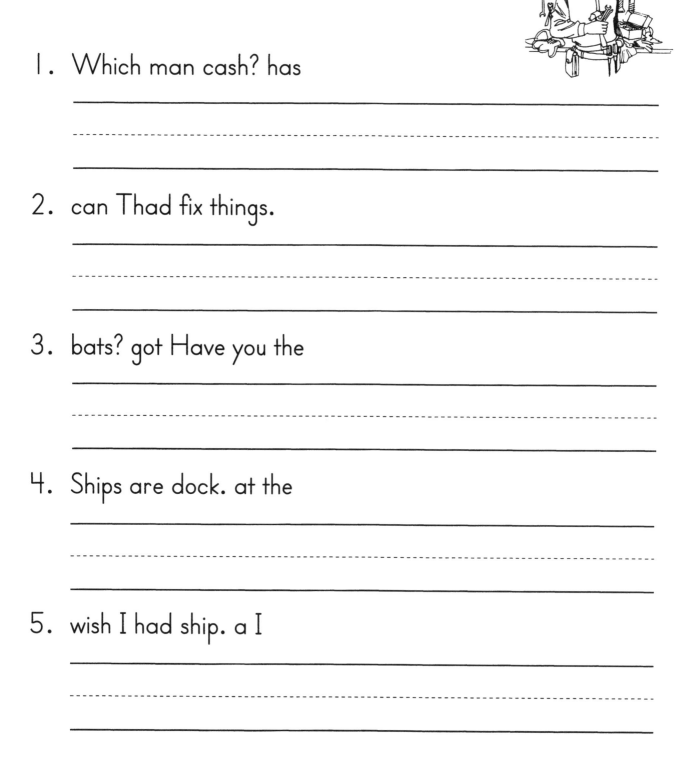

1. Which man cash? has

   _____

   -

   _____

2. can Thad fix things.

   _____

   -

   _____

3. bats? got Have you the

   _____

   -

   _____

4. Ships are dock. at the

   _____

   -

   _____

5. wish I had ship. a I

   _____

   -

   _____

Words in Alphabetical Order

Arrange these words in alphabetical order.

this, chill, ship, shock, think, rich, fish, cash, are, put

a b c d e f g h i j k l m n o p q r s t u v w x y z

1. _____

2. _____

3. _____

4. _____

5. _____

6. _____

7. _____

8. _____

9. _____

10. _____

Cloze Sentences

Find and circle the word that finishes each sentence.

1. Al got a whiff of the fish and _____.

   A) chips
   B) thicks

2. Thin Thad is the _____ who can fix things.

   A) chip
   B) chap

3. Thad has a _____ with kits, lids, mops, rags, and pans.

   A) ship
   B) shop

4. Chick has a _____ shop.

   A) lash
   B) fish

5. _____ Fish Shack is at the dock.

   A) Chick's
   B) Shop's

6. Lots of big _____ are at the dock.

   A) ships
   B) thins

7. _____ fish has Sam's dad got in his bag?

   A) When
   B) Which

Editor in Chief

Write a <u>C</u> on the line after the word if it is correct. If the word is spelled wrong, write it correctly on the line.

1. ths

_____

2. chil

_____

3. ship

_____

4. shock

_____

5. Thud

_____

6. inchh

_____

7. ar

_____

8. puut

_____

Story Writing

1. Write a story using some of the words from this unit.
2. If you wish, use another sheet of paper to draw pictures for your story or to make it longer.
3. Write a title for your story.

Unit Concept

<u>e</u>

Practice reading and spelling these words every day. Use the practice method your teacher shows you. Then use each word aloud in a sentence. You can do it!

bell	mess	them
chess	neck	then
get	pet	well
Jen	red	when
let	shell	yes

Word Monsters: *should, could, would*

Phoneme-Grapheme Correspondence Activity:
Phoneme Isolation 1

Listen to each word your teacher says. Underline the first sound you hear in each word.

1.   r   e   s

2.   t   p   f

3.   x   b   o

4.   a   s   qu

5.   i   d   g

6.   h   j   w

7.   f   a   l

8.   m   i   j

9.   m   s   r

10.   v   e   w

Phoneme-Grapheme Correspondence Activity:
Phoneme Isolation 2

Listen for the sound your teacher repeats, and circle the correct letter in each word.

1. bat

2. Sam

3. Tim

4. chip

5. egg

6. with

7. rod

8. when

9. ham

10. wish

11. jig

12. cat

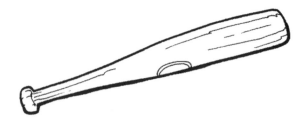

Writing Practice: e

Listen to your teacher's directions as you trace and copy this letter.
Put your pencil on the dot to begin.

e   •   •   •   •

e   •   •   •   •

e   •   •   •   •

e   •   •   •   •

Spelling Words Practice

1. Write and say each word three times.
2. Say the meaning or meanings for each word and use each word aloud in a sentence.

shell, let, then, pet, well, them, yes, Jen

1.

2.

3.

4.

5.

6.

7.

8.

red, chess, bell, neck, when, mess, get, could

9.

10.

11.

12.

13.

14.

15.

16.

should, would

17.

18.

Phoneme Segmentation

1. Read each word aloud.
2. Divide each word into beginning, middle, and ending sounds.
3. Write the entire word.

Read the Word	Divide the Sounds			Write the Word
	Beginning	Middle	End	
1. shell				
2. let				
3. then				
4. pet				
5. well				
6. them				
7. yes				

Phoneme Segmentation (continued)

Read the Word	Divide the Sounds			Write the Word
	Beginning	Middle	End	
	_____	_____	_____	_____
8. Jen	_____	_____	_____	_____
9. red	_____	_____	_____	_____
10. chess	_____	_____	_____	_____
11. bell	_____	_____	_____	_____
12. neck	_____	_____	_____	_____
13. when	_____	_____	_____	_____
14. mess	_____	_____	_____	_____
15. get	_____	_____	_____	_____

Spelling Words in Sentences

Use each word in a written sentence. Don't forget to use capital letters and correct ending punctuation.

shell, let, pet, them, yes, red, could

1.

2.

3.

4.

5.

6.

7.

Word Search

Find each hidden word. Some words might be hiding more than once, so make sure you mark them all!

1.	let	litletliroepdpletjditletioee
2.	then	theiruditlehthentheirthen
3.	yes	heirusldjyeityeutyesyesy
4.	when	htieuwhentheirlwhentheit

Matching

Draw a line from each word to the picture that matches it.

shell

pet

Jen

chess

bell

Picture-a-Word

1. Draw a picture for each of these words.
2. Use each word aloud in a sentence.

pet	neck
mess	red

Mixed-Up Words

Fix these mixed-up words and then write each one in a sentence.
Use the word list here to help you.

Wells, let, chess, mess, when, them, neck, red

1. tel

_____

2. elWls

_____

3. dre

_____

4. wneh

_____

Mixed-Up Words (continued)

Wells, let, chess, mess, when, them, neck, red

5. shecs

_____

- -

_____

_____

- -

_____

Mixed-Up Sentences

Fix these mixed-up sentences and write them correctly. (*Hint:* The words with the capital letters, question marks, and periods will help you.)

1. shop. pet Jen a has

   _____

   -

   _____

2. black Ted got a cat.

   _____

   -

   _____

3. fix could Ted ships.

   _____

   -

   _____

4. shell? Could have I a

   _____

   -

   _____

5. Sid off fell ship. the

   _____

   -

   _____

Words in Alphabetical Order

Arrange these words in alphabetical order.

shell, let, then, yes, Jen, red, chess, when, mess, could

a b c d e f g h i j k l m n o p q r s t u v w x y z

1. _____

2. _____

3. _____

4. _____

5. _____

6. _____

7. _____

8. _____

9. _____

10. _____

Cloze Sentences

Find and circle the word that finishes each sentence.

1. Miss Jen Wells has a big _____ shop at the dock.

   A) pat
   B) pet

2. Jen's pets could have a big _____ in the shop.

   A) mass
   B) mess

3. When the _____ rang, Jen fed the pets.

   A) sell
   B) bell

4. The ten labs _____ off the dock and got wet.

   A) fell
   B) tell

5. I think I should have a cat for a _____ at the shop.

   A) pat
   B) pet

6. When Ted was a lad, he _____ on a big ship.

   A) went
   B) will

7. The kids _____ the ship's cats fish in a pan.

   A) fed
   B) led

Editor in Chief

Write a <u>C</u> on the line after the word if it is correct. If the word is spelled wrong, write it correctly on the line.

1. shel

2. pet

3. shud

4. redd

5. ches

6. neck

7. wuld

8. wen

Story Writing

1. Write a story using some of the words from this unit.
2. If you wish, use another sheet of paper to draw pictures for your story or to make it longer.
3. Write a title for your story.